P9-CLF-817

ABE LINCOLN: FRONTIER BOY

Abe Lincoln
Frontier Boy

Stories Children Can Read

By
AUGUSTA STEVENSON

Illustrated by
CLOTILDE EMBREE

*"Only of such a boy were made
The loving man he was."*
—JAMES WHITCOMB RILEY

THE BOBBS-MERRILL COMPANY
PUBLISHERS   INDIANAPOLIS

Copyright, 1932

By The Bobbs-Merrill Company

Printed in the United States of America

PRESS OF
BRAUNWORTH & CO., INC.
BUILDERS OF BOOKS
BRIDGEPORT, CONN.

CONTENTS

FULL-PAGE ILLUSTRATIONS

ABE LINCOLN: FRONTIER BOY

A little boy in a little cabin

Abe Lincoln: Frontier Boy

I

THE BEGINNING

THERE was once a little boy in a little cabin on a little farm in a little clearing on a little creek. Now this little creek had a little name—*Knob*. But the boy had a big name—*Abraham*.

Little Knob Creek was in the great big state of Kentucky.

Little Abraham was in the great big family of Lincolns. There were his father, and mother, and little sister Sarah. There were many aunts and uncles. There were more cousins than he could count. He didn't see them very often but he knew about them.

They knew about Abe, too, and not one of them called him by his big name. "It is too long," they said. "Abe is better."

So Abe he was, even when he became a man and as long as he lived.

His father, Thomas Lincoln, was a poor man. He loved his children, but he couldn't give them nice clothes, or books, or toys.

Abe had one shirt and one pair of trousers. He had no shoes, so he went barefoot in the summer and wore moccasins in the winter. He had no hat, so he wore a coonskin cap the year round.

He had no books, or pictures, or toys. He saw nothing but the forest and the rough road

Abe Lincoln: frontier boy

that passed the cabin where the family lived.

And so, shut off from the world of cities and people and books and pictures, could Abe ever get out of the forest? Would the outside world ever hear of him?

No one at that time would have thought so, not even his parents.

But something wonderful was to happen to this poor little boy some day. Something so very wonderful it sounds like a fairy tale.

He was to become one of the greatest men this world has ever known. A great nation was to love him. The whole world was to hear of him and admire him.

And the kind of man he became was the kind of boy he was.

And the kind of boy he was will be told in these stories. Read them, boys and girls, and you will understand why Abe Lincoln became a great man and why every one loved and trusted him.

II

ABE'S FIRST TOY

1. Sarah's Doll

LITTLE Sarah Lincoln came into the cabin crying.

"Mother!" she said, "Abe won't play with me!"

Mrs. Lincoln was surprised. "What is the matter?" she asked. "Have you children been quarreling?"

"No, mother, we didn't quarrel, but Abe wouldn't play with my doll. It's a new doll, too, and it's the largest corn-cob father could find."

"That's true," said Mr. Lincoln. "It was the largest one in the field."

"It is a fine doll, Sarah," said mother. "Why doesn't Abe like it?"

"I don't know," said Sarah. "He said he wouldn't play girl games any more."

It is a fine doll

"Well! Well!" said mother.

"Ha, ha!" laughed father. "Abe is growing up, Nancy."

"But he is only five and a half, Thomas."

"He is growing up just the same. You must play something else with Abe, Sarah."

"There isn't anything else to play, father."

"If they only had some toys they could play better," said mother.

"I suppose they could," said father, "but toys

cost money and I haven't finished paying for this farm."

"Abe wants a little wagon," said Sarah.

"Couldn't you make one, Thomas?" asked Mrs. Lincoln. "You are such a good carpenter. You made our wooden plates."

"Of course I could make a little wagon," said Mr. Lincoln, "but I won't have time this summer. Maybe I can next winter."

"But Abe needs something to play with now," said mother. "He is so lonesome. Sarah helps me with the work and that leaves Abe alone so much. No little boys to play with. Nothing but just himself."

"I tell you what I'll do," said father. "I'm going to Thomas Hall's sale this morning to buy some tools, and if I can find a toy wagon I'll buy it. That is, if it doesn't cost too much."

"Oh, of course," said mother, "if it doesn't cost too much."

2. The Sale

The Hall family was going to move. Almost everything they owned was for sale, and people came from miles around to buy.

Mr. Lincoln met neighbors from up the creek and down the creek and over the hills.

They were all glad to see him. They liked him, and besides, he was the best judge of horses in that part of Kentucky.

"I've been waiting for you, Thomas," said a man. "I want to buy a horse but I want your opinion first."

Mr. Lincoln examined the horse carefully and told the man what it was worth.

Then other men asked him about horses and kept him busy so long he forgot all about that toy wagon for Abe.

At last he bought his tools and told his friends good-by.

As he went for his horse, two men passed him. They were carrying a long settee.

"I hope it will go in my wagon," said one.

"Wagon!" said Mr. Lincoln out loud. "Oh, yes! Wagon!" Then he hurried back to the cabin and began to look about.

On a table were dishes, forks, knives, spoons, buckets, pots and pans. On the floor were feather-beds, pillows, coverlids, quilts and skins. There seemed to be everything but toys.

"What are you looking for, Mr. Lincoln?" asked Mrs. Hall. "Perhaps I can help you."

"I want a little wagon for Abe, Mrs. Hall, but I don't see any toys."

Mrs. Hall laughed. "Look up there," she said.

She pointed to the shelf over the fireplace.

Mr. Lincoln looked up and then he laughed, for *there was a little toy wagon.*

"I have ten cents I can spend," he said.

"It's yours," said Mrs. Hall. "See! It's marked eight and one-half cents."

"Good!" said Mr. Lincoln. He paid the money, took the wagon, and started for the little log cabin on Knob Creek.

3. Abe Watches

Outside this cabin, on a stump, sat a little black-haired boy watching the road. He looked and he looked, but his father did not come.

His mother had said that father would be home for supper, but supper was over and he hadn't come. Now the sun was going down behind the hill. Soon it would be dark.

"Abe!" called Mrs. Lincoln from the door. "It's too late for you to be outside."

"May I wait till father comes?"

"No, Abe. It's too damp. You'll get fever and chills."

Abe went into the cabin at once.

"Why, Abe," said Sarah, "you're crying!"

"I want my wagon," said Abe.

Mother put her arms around the boy and spoke to him gently.

"Abe," she said, "father wasn't sure he could find a wagon, was he?"

"No," said Abe.

"And he wasn't sure he would have enough money to buy it, was he?"

"No," said Abe.

"Then you shouldn't be crying when he comes home. It will make him feel bad."

"I won't cry any more," said Abe.

"That's fine," said mother. "Sarah, Abe is a little man. Don't tell father he cried."

"I won't," said Sarah. "But father might lose the wagon on the way home."

"Lose it!" said Abe. "How could he lose it?"

"It might fall in the creek and he couldn't get

it out," said Sarah. "Or maybe he wouldn't even know it fell."

Abe's lips trembled. He looked as if he were going to cry again.

"Yes," said mother, "all of those things might happen."

She smiled at Abe, and Abe smiled back. Then he said bravely, "I won't cry anyway."

Just then the door opened and in came Mr. Lincoln.

"Here's your wagon, Abe!" he said.

"Oh!" said Abe. "Oh! Oh!"

And there wasn't a happier boy in the world than little Abe Lincoln that night.

III

SCHOOL-BUTTER

1. Before School

SARAH and Abe were ready for their first day of school. They were so excited they scarcely knew what they were doing. Sarah had braided her two pig-tails four times. Abe had combed his hair five times.

Sarah wore her new dress of linsey-woolsey that her mother had woven and made. She was barefooted and bareheaded. Her pig-tails hung down her back. She was a pretty little girl and she was good, too, and smart.

Abe wore his first pants. They were linsey-woolsey like his shirt and both were woven and made by his mother. He wore a coonskin cap but he was barefooted like Sarah.

Both children were as clean as soap and water could make them.

"Here are two corn-dodgers for your dinner," said mother. "Put them in your pocket, Sarah. If you children want berries you can pick them at noon. There are plenty in the woods around the schoolhouse."

"May I carry your speller, Sarah?" asked Abe.

"I don't care," said Sarah.

Just then Mr. Lincoln came in. "Sarah," he said, "tell the schoolmaster that I will buy a speller for Abe soon—the next time I go to a sale. He can study with you for a week or so."

"Don't I need a reader, too?" asked Sarah.

"Not until you have finished your speller," said mother.

"Be sure to study it out loud," said father. "The teacher won't know you are studying if you don't."

"All right," said Sarah, "I will."

"I will, too," said Abe.

"It's time to go," said mother. She kissed them, and father patted Abe's black head and Sarah's brown one.

The children followed the path across the yard and into the woods. Soon they were out of sight.

Mrs. Lincoln wiped the tears from her eyes.

Across the yard and into the woods

"It's so far for them to walk," she said. "Three miles every day and the path is rough."

"It can't be helped, Nancy. They are lucky to go to school at all. There are several children around here who can't afford it."

"We can't really afford it either," said Nancy.

"I'll do extra work this winter," said Thomas, "carpenter work. I think I'll make enough to pay the schoolmaster."

"I hope you will," said Nancy. "I'm so anxious for the children to learn."

"Yes," said Thomas Lincoln, "they must learn."

2. *After School*

Late that afternoon Sarah came home from school alone.

"Mother! Father!" she cried. "Abe's gone!"

"Gone!" said father. "Gone where?"

"I don't know," said Sarah. Then she began to cry.

"Come, come, dear, don't cry," said mother. "Sit here by me on the bench. Now then, tell us what happened."

"Just as school was out," said Sarah, "we heard some boys outside calling names at us."

"At you and Abe?" asked mother.

"No," said Sarah, "at all of us. I couldn't understand what they said but it made the schoolboys mad."

"Was it *School-butter?*" asked father.

"Yes, that was it! Then they ran, and our boys ran after them, and Abe went, too."

"Abe went!" cried mother, alarmed.

"I told him not to, but the boys called him. I guess he thought he had to go."

Mrs. Lincoln was frightened. "The big boys will run ahead and leave him," she said. "He will get lost in the woods."

"I'll go after him," said Mr. Lincoln. "Don't worry, Nancy, I'll find him."

Then he ran out of the cabin. He didn't even stop to get his cap.

Sarah cried again. "I'm afraid Abe will fall in the creek," she said.

Mother was afraid of that, too, but she didn't want Sarah to know it. So she said, "Father will find him. Now then, do you know why those boys called, *School-butter?*"

"No, mother, I don't."

"They wanted to make fun of the children who go to school."

"Why?" asked Sarah.

"I think they really want to go to school themselves but their folks can't afford it. So they pretend it's silly to go, sort of soft—like butter."

"Oh, yes," said Sarah. "I understand."

"Now let's get a good supper for father and Abe. I'll make some flour biscuits," said mother.

"Flour biscuits!" cried Sarah. And her eyes nearly popped right out of her head.

"It will be a treat for all of us," said mother. "Please put these apples in the hot ashes, Sarah. Then you may fill this gourd with maple-sugar."

"Oh! Oh!" said Sarah. "Won't that make Abe happy!"

3. Hunting Abe

Mr. Lincoln ran into the woods calling, "Abe! Abe!"

There was no answer so he ran up the trail toward the schoolhouse. Sometimes he stumbled over large tree roots. Once he caught his foot in a wild grapevine and fell. But in an instant he was up and running again.

He kept on calling Abe but there was only silence in the great forest.

At last he reached the clearing where the log schoolhouse stood. There wasn't a boy or a girl to be seen, so into the woods he went again. On and on up the trail he went.

"Abe!" he called again and again. "Abe! Abe! Abe!"

But there was no answer, and not even a glimpse of a little black-haired boy.

It began to get dark in the woods, but still Mr. Lincoln went on. At last he stopped.

"Abe couldn't have come any farther," he said to himself. "Abe couldn't walk any farther."

So he turned and went back on the trail toward the schoolhouse. He hoped the schoolmaster would still be there. He would go with him to hunt Abe. They would stop at every cabin on the creek and every neighbor would join them. They would all take torches and look in the creek.

Mr. Lincoln came to the clearing and went in the schoolhouse. There sat the master at his desk, writing.

"Mr. Riney!" said Mr. Lincoln, "I'm hunting Abe. He's lost!"

"Look there," said Mr. Riney, pointing to a bench.

Mr. Lincoln looked. There was Abe sound asleep!

"He ran after the boys," said Mr. Riney, "and

"I'm hunting Abe. He's lost!"

I ran after him and brought him back. I was just getting ready to take him home."

"I'm much obliged to you, Mr. Riney," said Mr. Lincoln. Then he went to Abe and shook him.

"Abe! Abe!" he said. "Wake up!"

Abe opened his eyes, but he was still half asleep.

"School-butter!" shouted the master.

Then Abe woke and jumped up.

The men laughed. Abe laughed. Then Mr. Lincoln took Mr. Riney and Abe to a very, very good supper in the Lincoln cabin on Knob Creek.

IV

GRANDFATHER LINCOLN AND THE INDIANS

1. Father Starts the Story

ONE rainy day Mother Nancy Lincoln was spinning wool.

Sarah and Abe were watching her. They loved to watch mother spin. They loved to watch that great wheel go round and round. They loved to see the spindle turn.

"Mother," said Abe, "I would rather watch you spin than do anything."

"So would I," said Sarah. "It's more fun than anything."

Mrs. Lincoln laughed. "I know something you both would rather do," she said. "You would much rather listen to your father tell stories."

Sarah and Abe didn't know what to say. They did love to hear father tell stories.

Mother laughed again. "That's all right, children," she said. "There isn't any one who can tell stories as well as your father. The neighbors all say that, and you know they visit us sometimes just to hear him."

"I know they do," said Sarah proudly.

"I'm going to tell stories, too, when I'm a man," said Abe.

Just then the door was opened quickly, and in came Father Thomas Lincoln with a gust of wind and rain. He was dripping wet: his clothes, his coonskin cap, his deerskin moccasins.

"This is a bad storm," he said. "I can't work in the field and I can't work in the woods. I can't even hunt or fish."

"It will give you a chance to rest," said Mrs. Lincoln. "Sarah, take your father's wet cap. Abe, take his moccasins."

Sarah hung the dripping cap on a peg in the wall *opposite* the fireplace. Abe put the dripping moccasins in a corner *away* from the fireplace.

Mr. Lincoln was pleased. "I see you children know how to take care of skins," he said, "as well as little Indians."

He sat on the fireside bench and soon his wet clothes began to dry.

"Would you like to hear a story, children?" he asked.

"Yes! Yes!" cried Sarah and Abe.

"Bring up your stools and I'll tell you a true story. It's about your Grandfather Abraham Lincoln."

"That's my name, too," said Abe.

"You were named for him," said Mr. Lincoln, "and I hope you will be as brave a man as he was."

"Wasn't he afraid of anything?" asked Abe.

"Nothing," said father, "not even Indians. He was a soldier in the Indian war."

"Did he wear a blue coat with brass buttons?" asked Sarah.

"Indeed he did," said father. "He was the captain of his company and he helped to drive the Indians out of these woods."

"Never forget that, children," said mother, "and always be good to soldiers."

"What could I do for a soldier?" asked Abe.

"You could take off your cap when you meet one," said father.

"You could get him a drink of water," said mother, "and give him some food."

"What do soldiers eat?" asked Sarah.

"Anything they can get," said father, "and plenty of that."

Mother laughed. The children laughed. Then father said, "Abe, throw a log on the fire, and I'll go on with the story."

2. *Father Finishes the Story*

Now Abe was only seven years old but he lifted a log and put it in the fireplace.

"Isn't Abe strong!" said Sarah.

"I like to be strong," said Abe. "I can help father in the field."

Father nodded. "Just as I helped my father when I was a little boy. In fact, that is part of my story. You see, children, my father was a farmer, too, just as I am, but he owned more land and horses and cows."

"We own horses," said Abe.

"We own cows," said Sarah, "and calves."

"Not half as many as my father had," said Mr. Lincoln, "and he owned more than two thousand acres of land."

"He must have been rich," said Sarah.

"No, Sarah, he wasn't rich. He worked in his fields every day, and my brothers and I worked with him. One spring morning when I was about six years old, he took me to a cornfield that was close to the woods."

"Were there Indians in the woods?" asked Abe.

"There had been, but father thought they would never return. The soldiers had built a fort near our farm and we felt quite safe.

"And so father stood there and looked over the field. 'Too many weeds,' he said. 'We'll pull them, Thomas.' He stooped over, but he didn't pull a single weed. Something terrible happened!"

"What? What?" cried Sarah and Abe.

"I heard a shot. I saw my father fall. He didn't speak again. He was dead."

"Indians!" said Abe.

"Indians!" said Sarah.

"Yes," said father, "Indians. They were hiding in the woods waiting for father to come out."

"Poor grandfather," said Sarah.

"They killed one of the best men in the country," said Mr. Lincoln. "And that wasn't all, children. They tried to get me."

"You!" cried the children.

"An Indian ran out of the woods and seized me. He began to drag me out of the field."

"Oh! Oh!" cried Sarah and Abe.

"I was frightened nearly to death. I thought I would never see my mother again."

"Poor little boy," said Mrs. Lincoln.

"We were now at the edge of the field. Another step or two and the Indian would have me in the woods. But again something happened! I heard another shot and I saw the Indian fall. He didn't speak or move. He was dead."

"Who shot him?" asked Abe.

"My oldest brother, and he was only twelve. He shot from our cabin door."

"But he might have killed you!" said Abe.

CLOTILDE EMBREE

"Then he dragged me

out of the field."

"The Indian had hold of you when your brother fired."

"He had to take the chance," said Mr. Lincoln. "My second brother had run to the fort for the soldiers. My mother could see other Indians in the woods and she was afraid I wouldn't reach the cabin alive.

"By that time the soldiers had come. They drove the Indians out of the woods and they never returned."

"I'm sorry about grandfather," said Abe, "but I'm glad that Indian didn't get you."

"I'm glad, too," said Sarah.

"I'm glad myself," said father.

"I'm gladdest of all," said mother.

V

SARAH AND ABE GO FISHING

"Mother," asked Abe, "do you need any more wood?"

"No, Abe," said Mrs. Lincoln, "you have brought all I need to-day."

"Do you need any more water?"

Mrs. Lincoln looked at the water buckets. "Why, they are full!" she said. "You must have worked pretty fast, Abe."

"I'd like to go fishing, mother."

"You have earned it, my dear boy. You may go and you may stay all the afternoon."

"I want to go, too," said Sarah.

"No," said mother, "you aren't old enough."

"I'm older than Abe," said Sarah. "I'm two years older."

"But Abe is larger and stronger, and he knows how to take care of himself."

Sarah began to cry.

"I'll take care of her," said Abe. "I won't let her go near the deep water."

"Very well then. Go along, children."

The children ran all the way to the creek. They had no fishing poles, or lines, or hooks, but they knew just what to do. They found a place where the creek was shallow and stooped over, holding their hands in the water.

"Don't let them slip through your hands," said Abe. "Fish are slippery."

Then they waited and waited and waited. Their arms ached and their necks and backs ached, but still they stooped and waited.

"Let's go home," said Sarah at last.

"Not yet," said Abe. "You can play on the bank, Sarah."

And Abe went on fishing.

Sarah found some acorns under a great oak tree. So for a long time she was very busy.

She made acorn cups and saucers. She made an acorn sugar bowl and cream pitcher. She made acorn bowls for berries and mush.

Then she played she was drinking sassafras tea from the cups. She used play cream and play sugar. She ate a bowl of play mush and a bowl of play berries.

Now she was tired of playing. "Abe!" she called. "Let's go home!"

"Not yet," said Abe. "Wait."

She made acorn cups and saucers

And Abe went on fishing.

Sarah looked about for something else to do. Her keen eyes found some wild grapes high on a large vine. The vine grew close by a giant tree and had fastened itself around it. It was almost as strong as the tree and as large around as Abe's arm.

So up that vine went Sarah, just like a little squirrel. Then she sat in a crook of the vine and ate grapes until she couldn't eat another one.

"Come on, Abe!" she called at last. "Let's go home!"

"Not yet," said Abe. "Wait."

And Abe went on fishing.

Sarah swung herself to the ground. Near by was a mother robin feeding a young robin. Sarah thought it would be fun to count the worms it ate. So she sat on a log, leaned against a tree, and began to count. "One, two, three, four, five, six, seven, eight, nine, ten, eleven . . ."

Some one was shaking her

Sarah's dark eyes closed. Sarah's brown head nodded.—Sarah was asleep.

And Abe went on fishing.

Sarah didn't know she went to sleep. She didn't know how long she slept. But she did know that some one was shaking her. She opened her eyes and there was Abe by her side.

"Look!" he said. "I've caught a fish!"

"It isn't very large," said Sarah.

"No, but it's a fish," said Abe, "and that's what I was fishing for."

"You were a long time," said Sarah.

"I don't care, I got it," said Abe. "Now then we'll go home."

VI

THE SOLDIER WITH BRASS BUTTONS

BACK home then went Sarah and Abe, through the woods with its great, great trees. And as they went along the trail, they talked and talked and talked.

Now what do you think they talked about? Bears? Wildcats? Snakes?

No indeed! They didn't even think of bears, and they didn't think of wildcats, or snakes.

They talked about Abe's fish. It was his first fish and he caught it with his hands. He was proud of that and he had a right to be proud. Just try to catch a fish with your hands. Sarah had tried. She knew how hard it was.

"Isn't your back tired, Abe?" she asked. "You had to lean over the water so long."

"Yes," said Abe, "but I don't care. I was determined to get a fish."

"Mother will be glad. She will fry it for our supper."

Just then some one called them. "Wait, children!" some one said.

The children turned. There was a strange man and he was coming toward them. He was smiling and waving his hand.

"I want to talk to you," he said. "I have been alone in this forest all day and I'm lonesome."

Abe looked at him and Abe's gray eyes opened wide. The man wore a blue coat with brass buttons!

Abe's cap came off quickly.

"Oh!" he said. "You are a soldier!"

"Yes," said the man. "I've been out fighting Indians."

"Oh, my!" said Sarah. "Indians!"

"You needn't be afraid," said the man. "They are far away from here."

"Can't I get you a drink of water?" asked Abe.

"Thank you, but I found a spring on the hill and I drank enough for a week."

Then he laughed, and Abe laughed, and Sarah laughed.

"Can't I get you something to eat?" asked Abe.

"I wish you could," said the soldier. "I'm hungry."

"Can't you come home with us to supper?" Sarah asked. "Mother would be glad to have you."

"So would father," Abe said. "His father was a soldier, too."

"Thank you both, but I must go on. I'll try to get some supper where I camp for the night. I'll find some grapes or berries."

"Take my fish, sir. You could cook it for your supper."

"No, no. my boy! Why, it's the only fish you have!"

"Please take it, sir. I want to do something for you."

"Why?" the man asked.

"Because you are a soldier," Abe said.

"Bless your kind heart!" the man said. "Yes, I'll take your fish, and I'll fry it for my supper. And thanks to you, little boy, many thanks."

"I want to be kind to all soldiers," said Abe.

"I hope you will be," said the man, "always as long as you live."

And Abe was kind to soldiers, *always, as long as he lived.*

VII

SAFETY FIRST

1. *Walking Lessons*

SOMETIMES Abe had a little boy to play with now. His name was Austin Gollaher, and he lived with his parents in a log cabin on Knob Creek.

It was three miles from the Lincoln cabin and the road was very rough. Up a steep hill, down a steep hill, over great roots and rocks and bumps.

So the two families couldn't visit very often. But whenever Mrs. Gollaher visited Mrs. Lincoln, she took Austin. And whenever Mrs. Lincoln visited Mrs. Gollaher, she took Abe.

Austin was two years older than Abe, but Abe was now so large and strong he could do everything Austin could.

The boys had great fun together. They

played in the woods around their cabins. They played in the creek near their cabins, but deep into the forest, away from the trails, they were never allowed to go.

"You boys must wait until you learn the forest," said Mr. Lincoln. "It is full of danger."

"Yes, indeed," said Mr. Gollaher, "there is great danger to all who do not understand her language."

"Language!" said Austin. "What do you mean?"

"How can a forest have a language?" asked Abe.

"The forest has many sounds and warnings and you must know what they mean," said Mr. Gollaher. "When you learn that, you will know her language."

"And if you don't obey her warnings, you may never get out alive," said Mr. Lincoln.

The boys were obedient. Not once did they run away to play in the deep woods.

Several months passed. Then one day Mr. Lincoln said, "Boys, you are old enough now to study the forest. When do you want to begin your lessons?"

"Now, father," said Abe, "if that suits you."

"Yes," said Austin, "now, Mr. Lincoln, if you please."

First, Mr. Lincoln taught them to walk like Indians without making a noise. They learned to keep away from dry leaves and broken twigs. They learned to pass bushes without breaking off a leaf. They learned to cover their tracks and to follow the tracks of others.

Mr. Lincoln showed them how to hide and how to crawl so quietly one could scarcely see the grass move.

All this was not learned in one day. The boys practised weeks and weeks.

At last Mr. Lincoln was satisfied.

"You boys do very well," he said, "as well as Indian boys of your age."

2. *Listening Lessons*

Then Mr. Lincoln taught the boys to listen to the sounds in the forest. "You must know all the cries and sounds of birds and beasts," he said, "whether they mean pleasure, or anger, or hunger."

He taught them the cries of the eagle and panther; the hiss of the snake and its rattle; the scream of the wildcat and the different growls of the bear.

It took a long, long time to learn these sounds. It was as hard as your arithmetic, but the boys kept at it, and after a while their ears were as sharp as razors.

When a wild bird called they could answer. They could hoot almost as well as a screech owl.

But when they heard the cry of an eagle, they knew they had to hide. And when they heard a rattle, they ran straight home to their mothers.

3. Tracking Lessons

From Mr. Gollaher the boys learned the tracks of animals, birds and snakes. This took a long time, too. It was harder than your geography. But the boys kept at it, and after a while, their eyes were as sharp as their ears.

They followed a fox's track to his den and saw the handsome fellow.

They followed a rabbit's tracks to her nest and saw the baby rabbits.

They followed deer tracks to a pool and saw the pretty deer drinking.

They followed the tracks of a ground-hog and saw him digging his home.

They followed the tracks of a beaver and saw him cutting a tree.

Some tracks they did not follow.

"Boys," said Mr. Gollaher, "when you see bear tracks you must go the other way. And you must never follow the tracks of panthers or wildcats."

The boys obeyed him. They knew now that it was *Safety First* in the forest.

They learned to notice everything. If a twig was broken they saw it. If the moss was crushed they knew it. Their eyes grew sharper and sharper.

One day they thought they saw a log move. Did they run to the log and jump on it? Did they scream or laugh aloud?

No indeed! They hid behind a tree and watched. Not one word did they speak. Not one sound did they make.

The log moved again and what do you think came out of it? Why, a big, black bear!

What do you think came out of it?

The two boys ran home, and they ran just as fast as their legs could carry them.

You see, they had learned to *Stop*, and *Look*, and *Listen*. They had learned *Safety First*.

VIII

THE CRY IN THE WOODS

ONE summer day, Abe and Austin were playing in the woods. They swung in a grapevine swing. They swung up into the blue sky and far out over the wide creek.

It was great fun. They smiled, and laughed, and sang, and whistled.

Then Austin said, "Let's play Indian."

"All right," said Abe. "Let's go to the cave. It's the best place in the world to play Indian."

They jumped to the ground and started toward the cave.

"You're right," said Austin. "That cave is the best place in the world to——"

Just then they heard a strange sound—a cry. Both boys stopped instantly.

"What was that?" whispered Austin.

"It sounded like a baby crying."

"A baby out here in the woods! There couldn't be, Abe."

"Of course not, Austin. I said it sounded like one."

Then they heard the cry again.

"I can't understand it," said Austin.

"It comes from those bushes," said Abe. "I'm going to see what it is."

Austin seized Abe's arm. "Don't go over there!" he said. "It might be a panther. A panther can cry just like a child."

"But it might be something that is hurt," said Abe.

"I think it's a panther, Abe. I wouldn't go near those bushes—not for all the money in the world."

"I'll wait till it cries again," said Abe.

"S—sh!" said Austin. "There it is!"

"I know it's something that is hurt," said Abe. "It has that kind of sound. I'm going!"

He ran toward the bushes. Austin waited just one minute, then he followed. He couldn't hang back when his chum went on.

The boys had reached the bushes when they heard the cry again. It was there—where they stood.

They parted the branches and there was something that was hurt. There lay a little dog with a broken leg.

"Poor doggie, poor doggie," said Abe.

"Poor doggie."

"Poor doggie," said Austin.

The little dog looked at them. Then he cried again and again.

"Don't cry, doggie," said Abe. "I'll fix your leg. I know how."

He made a splint of bark. Then he put the broken leg into the splint and tied it with strips of soft bark.

Austin watched him. "I wish I knew how to make a splint," he said.

"Father showed me," said Abe.

The poor little dog stopped crying and licked Abe's hand. That was his way of saying, "Thank you, little boy. You are so good to me."

"Let's hide him in our cave," said Abe, "till he can walk."

"The very thing!" said Austin. "I'll go on ahead and make a bed of leaves."

Abe lifted the dog gently and carried him to

the cave. He laid him upon the bed of leaves
gently and patted his head.

"I'll take care of him," said Abe. "I live
nearer the cave than you do, Austin."

"I'd look after him if I could," said Austin.
"You know that, don't you, Abe?"

"Of course I know it," said Abe. "You
wouldn't let the poor dog go hungry any more
than I would."

Then the boys patted the dog again and went
away.

That evening Abe took food and water to the
dog. He fed him every day. He gave him
fresh water every day. He made a new bed of
leaves every day. As soon as the dog could walk
Abe took him home. The broken leg was
crooked, but it was strong.

Abe named him *Honey* because he loved him
dearly. And the dog loved Abe dearly and followed him everywhere.

IX

KEEN EYES

M<small>R. LINCOLN</small> came into the cabin and looked about the room. He saw Mrs. Lincoln getting supper. He saw Sarah helping, but he didn't see Abe.

"Where is Abe?" he asked.

"I sent him to Mrs. Brown's with some venison," said Mrs. Lincoln.

"When did he go?"

"At noon, just after dinner. He should be home by this time."

"Of course he should," said Mr. Lincoln. "He is playing in the woods."

"It's a long way to the Browns' and back, Thomas, and there are two steep hills to climb."

"I know, but he should have been here an hour ago. I want him to help me with a log. I can't lift it alone, and the fire is almost out."

Then Mr. Lincoln sat in front of the dying fire and waited. Ten minutes passed, fifteen, twenty.

Supper was ready, but every one waited for Abe.

It was now quite dark and Mrs. Lincoln was worried. "I wonder what makes him so late," she said.

"He is always late," said Mr. Lincoln. "He thinks of nothing but play."

"He doesn't really play, father," said Sarah. "He just stops to look at things."

"What things?" asked Mr. Lincoln.

"Oh, trees, and clouds, and grass, and stones."

Mr. Lincoln frowned. "It's all nonsense," he said. "It's a bad habit."

Suddenly Mrs. Lincoln smiled. "I heard him whistle to Honey," she said. "He'll be here in a minute."

Sure enough, just then Abe and Honey came

out of the dark woods. In another minute they were in the cabin and Abe was hanging his cap on a peg.

"Mrs. Brown said she was much obliged for the venison," Abe said to his mother.

"You should have been home an hour ago," said his father.

"I didn't know it was so late. I was looking at something."

"You are always looking at something," said Mr. Lincoln angrily. "You must come straight home when you are sent on an errand."

"I'll try not to be late again," said Abe.

"What were you looking at?" asked Sarah.

"That tall poplar tree on the top of our hill."

"You've seen it a hundred times," said Mr. Lincoln.

"But I never noticed how it looked at night. It leans over, you know, father."

"Well, what if it does?"

"Why, it leans right across the smoke that comes from Mr. Brown's chimney."

"Did you watch that for an hour?" asked Mr. Lincoln.

"I watched it a long time. I wanted to see if the smoke was always back of the tree. And it was. It was pretty, too—just like a picture, mother."

"I must look at it some night," said sweet Nancy Lincoln.

"There's no sense in looking at trees and smoke," said Mr. Lincoln. "I want it stopped, Abe."

"I'll come straight home the next time, father."

"Supper is ready!" said Mrs. Lincoln.

"No supper till there is a log in the fireplace," said Mr. Lincoln. "Come along, Abe, and help me."

X

THE FIRE

ONE dark night a neighbor rushed into the Lincoln cabin. He didn't knock. He didn't remove his cap. He didn't speak to Mrs. Lincoln or Mr. Lincoln. He didn't speak to Sarah or Abe. He didn't tell them why he carried a large water bucket. He didn't say why the bucket was empty.

He just stood in the door and shouted, "Fire! Fire! Brown's cabin is on fire!"

"I'll be ready in one minute," said Mr. Lincoln.

"So will I," said Abe.

Now the Brown family lived some distance from the Lincolns, but that didn't make any difference. Settlers always helped one another when there was trouble.

So Mr. Lincoln seized a large bucket and

Mrs. Lincoln gave him his cap. Abe seized another bucket and Sarah gave him his cap.

Then out ran Mr. Lincoln and the neighbor, and out ran Abe after them.

"I want to go, too!" cried Sarah.

"No, Sarah," said mother, "you must stay here with me."

"But I've never seen a fire," said Sarah. "Please let me go!"

"There's a creek to cross. Could you run over the log in the dark?"

And they ran across

Sarah hung her head. Mother went on: "The others will. Then they will climb the steep hills like rabbits, and leave you far behind."

"I'll stay here with you, mother," said Sarah.

It was just as Mrs. Lincoln had said. The two men and Abe crossed the creek in the dark. And they ran across the log, too!

Then came a steep hill and up they went like rabbits. Sometimes Abe slipped and fell, but he didn't mind that. He reached the top.

the log, too!

They could see the smoke plainly now, great clouds of it floating into the dark sky.

"Yes, it's Brown's cabin," said the neighbor. "There's no doubt of that."

"Not a bit!" said Mr. Lincoln. "Come on!"

"Wait!" said Abe. "Don't go!"

The men were astonished. They turned and looked at Abe. He was standing near a large poplar tree and was pointing to it.

"Look at this tree," he said. "Do you see any smoke back of it?"

"That's nonsense," said Mr. Lincoln. "Stop looking at that tree and come on."

"There's no use to go," said Abe. "The Brown cabin isn't burning. The smoke from their chimney is always just back of this poplar tree. The tree bends over across it. I've seen it at night and it looked pretty."

"That is true," said Mr. Lincoln. "He told us about it some time ago."

Abe pointed to the smoke. "That smoke is south of this tree," he said. "It's a long way from Mr. Brown's cabin."

"Then whose cabin is it?" asked the neighbor.

"It isn't a cabin," said Abe. "That fire is in a grove on Mr. Brown's farm. He must be burning logs."

"That's right," said the neighbor. "He told me he was going to burn them, and I forgot all about it. Abe, you have saved us a long, hard trip."

Then back down the hill went the two men and Abe. The men were silent. Abe was afraid his father was angry.

At the foot of the hill the neighbor stopped. "Abe," he said, "how did you know that poplar tree leaned across the smoke from Mr. Brown's chimney?"

"I saw it one night and I watched it so long I was late for supper," said Abe.

"And I scolded him and told him to stop watching things," said Mr. Lincoln. "I see now that I made a mistake."

"A big mistake, Thomas," said the neighbor. "Let Abe watch things, and he'll make one of the smartest men who ever came out of these Kentucky hills."

And Mr. Lincoln didn't scold Abe for stopping to look at things—not for a long time.

XI

THANK HONEY

THE miller came to the door of his mill. "Abe!" he called, "your corn meal is ready."

He waited for a moment, but Abe didn't come.

The miller called again. "Abe! Abe Lincoln! Your corn meal is ready."

He waited again for a moment, but Abe didn't come.

The miller couldn't understand this. Abe often brought his father's corn to the mill, and he always waited until it was ground.

Once he had to wait all day. But he didn't complain and he didn't go home till the meal was ready.

No wonder the good miller was puzzled. He was just a bit angry, too. Here were several men waiting to have their corn ground, and here he must spend his time looking for Abe.

The men were talking outside. Now they were coming up to the mill. They didn't like this delay either. No doubt they were all in a hurry. They always wanted to get home before dark.

They were crossing a little foot-bridge close to the mill, and he could see their faces. To his great surprise not one of them looked angry. In fact they all seemed worried.

Their voices were anxious, too, when they spoke to him.

"Abe isn't around here," said one. "I saw him go into the woods a long time ago."

"So did I," said another. "His dog was with him."

"I saw him, too," said another. "I had just come."

"How long ago was that?" asked the miller.

"Oh, it was an hour or so, I guess."

"All of an hour," said the first man.

"Then I'm afraid he's lost," said the miller.
"He's only seven years old."

"Only seven!" said the third man. "Does he
bring his father's corn to the mill?"

"Yes," said the miller. "He rides a horse
bareback, with the corn in a sack behind him.
And he pays me every penny and takes the corn
meal home."

"My boy couldn't do that," said the fourth
man, "and he's eight."

"Abe is a big boy for his age," said the second
man.

"He is too smart to be lost," said the first
man. "And he knows his way through the
forest."

"Yes, and he knows he ought to be back,"
said the miller.

"Then something has happened to him," said
the second man. "Bears with cubs are ugly just
now."

"He rides a horse bareback, with the corn in a sack behind him."

"Wildcats and panthers are always ugly," said the first man.

"We must hunt for him," said the miller.

"Yes! Yes!" said the men.

"Lead the way," said the miller to the first man. "You saw where he entered the woods."

"Follow me!" said the first man.

In single file they crossed the little foot-bridge and passed the great mill wheel. They went down the brook and through the clearing. They were now at the edge of the woods.

"This is where he went in," said the first man.

"Lead on," said the others.

But just then something happened! Something that made every one of those men stop in his tracks.

A little dog came running out of the woods!

"Honey!" cried the miller.

"Honey!" cried the others.

Yes, it was Honey. He barked sharply. He

leaped up to the miller's outstretched hand and touched it with his paw.

His eyes were troubled and anxious. Everything he did and the very sound of his bark said as plainly as words, "Abe's in trouble! Help! Help!"

Honey ran to the other men and looked up into their faces with his soft, anxious eyes. He barked sharply again and again.

Then he ran back into the woods. Suddenly he stopped and looked at the men again, and again he barked sharply. He was talking to them. He was saying, "Come on! Come on! Follow me!"

"He wants us to follow him," said one man. "See how he turns and looks at us."

"Something has happened to Abe," said another man, "and Honey has come to tell us."

"He'll lead us to Abe," said another man. "Come on!"

The men followed Honey. He led them far into the woods. At last he stopped at a cave. He looked at the men and barked. Then he ran into the cave.

The men followed him. Then they heard a boy's voice calling.

"That's Abe!" said the miller. "I know his voice."

"We're coming, Abe! We're coming!" shouted the men.

Very soon they found him. He could talk, but he couldn't move. He was held fast between two great rocks.

"Why, Abe," said the miller, "what has happened here?"

"I climbed up on this rock," said Abe. "Then all at once that large rock fell. I was caught between them and I couldn't move."

"It might have fallen on you," said one of the men.

The men worked carefully. Slowly they rolled the rock away and at last Abe was free.

He thanked the men for saving him.

"Don't thank us," they said. "Thank Honey!"

Then Honey barked and barked. That was his way of saying, "I brought these men here. I told them about you."

The men laughed at Honey and patted him. Abe patted him, too, but he didn't laugh.

"My goodness!" he said. "What if that rock had fallen on Honey!"

XII

MOVING TO INDIANA

Two tired horses came slowly along the road. On one was pretty dark-eyed Mrs. Nancy Lincoln. In front of her rode Sarah. Abe rode the other horse with a great bundle of household goods behind him. Mr. Lincoln walked by the horses.

All day long they had traveled, and the day before, and the day before that, too.

"Why don't we come to the big river?" asked Sarah.

"I thought we would make it by evening," said Mr. Lincoln, "but we can't, the horses are too tired. We'll camp in the first good place. And here it is! A spring by the side of the road! This is good luck. Whoa! Whoa!"

In another minute every one was busy. Mr. Lincoln fed and watered the horses. Then he

Two tired horses came

CLOTILDE EMBREE

slowly along the road

gathered wood and made a fire. Mrs. Lincoln fried bacon and corn-cakes. Abe gathered leaves and made beds on the ground. Sarah took coverlids from the great bundle and laid them on the leaves.

By that time supper was ready and the Lincoln family sat on a log and ate. Oh, how good the bacon and corn-cakes! How cool the sparkling spring water!

They talked about the home they had left on Knob Creek. They were all sorry to leave it.

"But our new home will be prettier," said mother. "Our cabin will be on a little hill."

"Children," said father, "there are walnut and hickory trees all over the place."

"I love walnuts," said Sarah.

"So do I," said Abe, "and I love hickory nuts, too. But I'm sorry I have to leave Austin."

"Austin can visit us," said mother.

"And best of all," said father, "corn grows

better in Indiana. So I'll make more money than I did in Kentucky."

"Oh, I'm sure you will, Thomas," said mother. "And now, children, it's time for bed."

"Will you keep the fire burning all night?" asked Sarah.

"Yes, indeed," said father. "There are many wild animals in these woods."

"May I help watch?" asked Abe.

"I may call you later. I'll watch first."

The others got ready for bed. It took only a moment. They just rolled up in their coverlids, clothes and all, and were soon fast asleep.

Suddenly Abe heard his father call him. It was his turn to watch, so he jumped out from his covers and went to the fire.

"Why, this isn't any fire at all," he said. Then he piled on wood until he had it blazing.

"No beast will come near this fire," he said. "They can see it far away."

Then he piled on more wood and kept it blazing for a long time.

Suddenly he noticed that the fire was going out. He looked for wood but there was no more. He was frightened.

"What shall I do?" he thought. He didn't dare go into the dark forest for wood.

The blaze went out. The fire was only smoking now. All around was a wall of darkness—black, black darkness.

And now in this wall of black Abe saw two green spots of light. The eyes of some wild animal! And they were coming toward him! Nearer and nearer they came!

"Father!" he called. "Father! Father!"

Some one was now shaking him. "Wake up! Wake up!" his father said.

Abe opened his eyes. It was just daylight. The fire was burning. Bacon and corn-cakes were frying.

"Why, I thought I let the fire go out," said Abe. "I saw two green eyes watching me."

"You had a bad dream," said mother.

"Didn't I watch the fire at all?"

"No," said father, "your mother and I took turns."

"I'm glad it was a dream," said Abe, "but I learned how to keep a fire burning all night."

"How?" asked father.

"A low fire, no blaze, and just a little wood at a time."

"Why, that boy learns in his sleep," said father.

They all laughed. Then Abe crawled out of his coverlid and Sarah crawled out of hers. They washed at the spring and combed their hair. Then they were ready for breakfast.

Again the Lincoln family sat on the log and ate bacon and corn-cakes.

Then on they went, on toward the beautiful Ohio River, and their new home.

XIII.

THE NEW HOME

1. *Into the Wilderness*

THE beautiful Ohio River had been crossed. A ferry-boat had taken the Lincoln family over, horses and all, to the Indiana shore.

Mr. Lincoln hired a big wagon and hitched up his horses. The others threw the bundles in and sat on them. Then off they drove into the wilderness.

Mrs. Lincoln and the children had never seen such a dense forest. There was no end to it.

They had to travel slowly, for the road wasn't much more than a path. At times Mr. Lincoln had to cut away tree branches so the wagon could pass on.

Of course Abe helped. He knew how to handle an ax and had helped his father in Kentucky.

The road was very rough. Sometimes the wagon bumped over great roots and then the whole family would bounce into the air.

But that didn't worry the Lincolns. The more they bounced the more they laughed.

"It's fun to bounce," said Abe. "I like it."

"So do I," said Sarah.

Now a wide creek had to be crossed. The children watched the water creeping up, closer and closer to the wagon-bed and were frightened.

Mother didn't seem to like it, either. "Thomas!" she called. "The water will come into the wagon!"

"Oh, that won't hurt anything," said Mr. Lincoln. "We can dry everything in the sun."

"Why, of course we can," said mother. "I didn't think of that."

"And your feet won't melt if the water does cover them," said father. "You're neither sugar nor salt."

"That's true," said mother. "We'll just play we are wading in the creek, children."

What fun those two children had then! The water did come into the wagon, up to their ankles and they could wade sitting still.

After that, they were anxious to cross wide creeks.

So on they went, farther and farther into the great wilderness. On they went, bumping, bouncing, wading and laughing.

2. The Log Cabin

At last they reached Mr. Lincoln's land. There was no clearing, no cabin, no shelter of any kind. There was nothing but the dense, dense forest.

The children had no time to be afraid of Indians or wild animals. They had to go to work at once.

Every day Abe worked with his father

Mr. Lincoln and Abe cut down small trees and made a shed with the poles. It wasn't much of a home, but it was a shelter from rain and snow.

Then came the new log cabin. Large trees had to be chopped down and made into logs. The logs had to be cut certain lengths. Large stumps had to be pulled up or burned.

It was all hard work and it was cold and wet, but every day Abe worked with his father.

Mrs. Lincoln and Sarah had to find the food. Mrs. Lincoln could shoot almost as well as Mr. Lincoln. Sometimes it was a deer. Sometimes a squirrel or rabbit.

The front of the shed had been left open and in this opening they had their fire. And here they did their cooking.

At last the cabin was almost finished. The floor wasn't laid and the windows and door weren't made, but the Lincolns moved in anyway. It was better than the shed, and mother said they could get along for a while, until father had finished clearing land for a corn-field.

Mother liked the new cabin because it was in such a beautiful place. It stood on a slight elevation in the midst of large forest trees. It was shaded by walnut and hickory trees. Near by were papaw and sassafras trees.

There were wild grapevines and spice bushes and many kinds of wild berries.

All this delighted Mrs. Lincoln. "Thomas," she said, "you have chosen a beautiful spot for our home."

She hung a bearskin over that open doorway and spread deerskins upon the cold earth floor.

In the evening after the day's work was done

the Lincoln family sat before a blazing fire in the large fireplace.

Sometimes Sarah and Abe ate walnuts or hickory nuts. Sometimes they just sat still and listened to father tell Indian stories until mother said, "Time for bed, children!"

Then up the pegs in the wall went Abe. He slept in the loft on a pile of sweet-smelling leaves, covered with a thick wool coverlid. He had no pillow but he had a bearskin over him and he was warm and happy.

They were all happy together. The cabin was a dear place to them. It was home and they loved it.

XIV

MOTHER NANCY LINCOLN

Yes, Mother Nancy Lincoln liked their new home, but there was something she did not like. There was no school in the Pigeon Creek Settlement, and mother wanted her children to go to school.

She had gone to school herself when she was a girl, and she could read and write. She had learned to love good books, and she wanted Sarah and Abe to love them.

But what could she do? There wasn't a school within ten miles.

"Well," she said, "we will have school here at home and I will be the schoolmaster."

The children hadn't gone to school in Kentucky very long, and they had forgotten all they had learned. So Mrs. Lincoln began with their letters. Then she taught them spelling and reading and a little arithmetic.

She told them Bible stories and read the Bible to them.

She taught them to be honest and tell the truth.

She taught them nice ways and good manners.

Abe learned to take off his coonskin cap when he entered a cabin. He learned to stand until older persons were seated.

Both children learned to say, "Thank you," and "Good morning," and "Good night."

Indeed, Sarah and Abe had such nice ways that later on, other settlers liked to have the children visit them.

And so the school went on. Mrs. Lincoln gave the children all the time she could, but she was too busy to give them all the time they needed.

But she found out several things. She found that while both children were smart and learned quickly, Abe was the one who really loved to study. So she made up her mind to one thing—Abe should go to school.

Mr. Lincoln didn't agree with her. He had never gone to school himself, and he couldn't read or write.

"If Abe knows how to cut down trees and raise corn, that's enough," he said.

"No, Thomas, it isn't enough. Abe is not like other boys. He is more serious and he asks such smart questions about things."

"He asks too many questions. I tell him to get to work."

"Because you can't answer him and neither can I," said Mrs. Lincoln. "And that's just the reason he should have a real teacher, some one who can tell the boy what he wants to know."

"Well, there isn't any school near enough, Nancy, so that settles it."

"No, Thomas, it doesn't. There is a way—we'll move near a school."

"And begin all over again? Build a new cabin and clear new land?"

"Yes," said that determined young mother. "We'll begin all over again."

Just then Abe came into the cabin.

"Abe," said mother, "we are talking about sending you to school."

"You don't want to go, do you?" asked father. "You'd rather work in the field, wouldn't you?"

"No," said Abe. "I'd rather go to school and work with books."

"Abe, you shall go to school next winter if I live," said Nancy Lincoln.

But Nancy Lincoln didn't live. She died the very next fall.

A little girl and two boys sat in the Lincoln cabin
and looked into the fire

XV

LONESOME CHILDREN

ONE night a little girl and two boys sat in the
Lincoln cabin and looked into the fire.

They were alone in the cabin. And the great
dark forest was like a wall of darkness that shut
them in and held them fast.

How would you like that if you were only nine and one-half like Abe, or only almost eleven like Sarah, with only an older boy to stay with you?

Do you think these two children liked it? Listen to what they said and you will know.

For a long time they didn't say anything. They just sat on stools and looked into the fire.

At last Sarah said, "It's lonesome here."

"It's mighty lonesome," said Abe.

"I guess you miss your mother," said the older boy.

"I miss her all the time, Cousin Dennis," said Sarah.

"So do I," said Abe.

"I miss her, too," said Dennis. "Look how she had me come here to live when my mother died. And she was always good to me, too."

"She was good to every one," said Sarah.

"She was good herself," said Abe.

"I'm glad you are here, Dennis," said Sarah. "I'm sorry the cabin isn't as clean as mother kept it." She looked at the untidy room.

"You work too hard, Sarah," said Dennis. "I wish I could help you more."

"I bring in all the water and wood," said Abe.

"You both do all you can," said Sarah quickly. "You have too much work yourselves since father went away."

"We are trying to finish that rail fence before he gets back," said Dennis.

"We want to surprise him," said Abe.

"He said he wouldn't be gone long, but it's a month to-day," said Sarah.

"That isn't long," said Abe. "He had to walk, and it's a hundred miles to Knob Creek."

"And a hundred miles back," said Dennis, laughing.

But Sarah didn't even smile. "Anyway, I think it's queer he went away and left us alone."

"It is queer," said Dennis.

Abe didn't say anything, but he thought it was queer, too.

Then they stopped talking and looked into the fire again. It burned low; it went out.

"It's time to go to bed," said Sarah.

"Good night," said Dennis, and up the pegs he went to the loft.

"Good night," said Abe, and up he followed Dennis.

Sarah went to bed in the untidy room below. All was quiet in the cabin.

Now the forest began to speak her language of sounds and warnings. An owl hooted, and Sarah hid her head under her quilt.

A wildcat screamed and Abe crept closer to Dennis in their bed of leaves.

No wonder these children were lonesome.

Wouldn't you have been lonesome, too?

XVI

WHAT THE BIG WAGON BROUGHT

Another day went by, and then another, and another. Still Mr. Lincoln did not return, and still the three were alone in the cabin.

But they went on with their work, the boys in the woods splitting rails and Sarah in the cabin.

She tried so hard to get good meals for Abe and Dennis, but nothing she cooked was just right. The mush was too thin. The corn-cakes were too hard. The meat was either burned or raw.

She tried to wash the heavy bed-clothes, but she couldn't lift them.

She was discouraged. Every day she cried and cried.

Then suddenly everything was changed. One morning a big wagon came through the woods to the Lincoln cabin.   A wagon drawn by four horses!

Out of the cabin rushed Sarah.   Out of the woods rushed Dennis and Abe.   And out of the wagon jumped Thomas Lincoln!

"Children," he said, "I have brought you a present from Kentucky.   I have brought you a new mother."

A tall pretty woman jumped from the wagon and ran toward them.   She had fair curly hair and the sweetest smile.

"Children!" she cried.   "Children!"   With that she hugged them and kissed them and told them they were her children now and she had come to take care of them.

"You will be just like my own children to me," she said.   "You are all about the same age and you will have a good time together."

Then this lively lady turned toward the wagon and called, "John!   Matilda!   Sarah!"

At once the three Johnston children jumped from the wagon and smiled at Abe, and Sarah, and Dennis.

And Abe and Sarah and Dennis smiled at John and Matilda and Sarah Johnston.

"Now, children," said Mrs. Lincoln, "please take everything out of the wagon and carry it into the cabin."

Six happy young people began to unload the big wagon. There were great bundles of feather-beds, pillows, quilts, wool coverlids, sheets, towels and clothing.

"The bureau next!" called Mrs. Lincoln. "And do please be careful!"

"My goodness!" said Sarah Lincoln. "A bureau! I never saw one before."

John, Dennis and Abe carried it into the cabin. You would have thought they were carrying eggs—they were so careful.

"It's beautiful," said Abe.

CLOTILDE EMBREE

"And do please

be careful!"

"It makes the cabin look fine," said Dennis.

"Wait till you see the chairs," said Matilda. "They have backs."

"Backs!" cried Sarah and Abe and Dennis.

They ran to the wagon and soon six chairs stood in the cabin; six chairs with backs.

"Oh! How beautiful!" cried Sarah Lincoln. "It's the finest cabin on Pigeon Creek now. Isn't it, boys?"

"It is," said Abe.

"It is," said Dennis.

How that new mother worked! Here, there and everywhere, just like the general of an army. And she had her army working, too.

Clean bed-clothes went on the beds. Dishes, knives, forks and spoons were scoured. Pots and pans were scoured. The table, benches and stools were scrubbed. Soon everything was so clean it just couldn't be any cleaner.

Next, Mrs. Lincoln began on Sarah and Abe.

Soon they were so clean they just couldn't be any cleaner.

Then she gave Sarah a pretty new dress. She gave Abe new shirts and trousers. She gave them both new shoes—not moccasins—shoes. She made two sad children so happy they didn't know themselves.

That night Abe and Dennis slept on a feather-bed in the loft. Clean pillows were under their heads and clean quilts covered them. How happy they were! How Abe loved this new mother!

And that wasn't all. Mrs. Sarah Johnston Lincoln told Mr. Thomas Lincoln that she wanted a wooden floor, windows and a door. And she told him so plainly he couldn't mis-understand, so he just went to work and made them.

He was a good carpenter, you know, and now he had three boys to help him. So it wasn't long until there was a beautiful clean floor and a door and windows.

Never again was that cabin a lonely place. Six children helped with the work. Six children laughed and talked. Six children popped corn, roasted apples and cracked nuts.

But best of all to Sarah and Abe was to have that kind new mother.

XVII

ABE'S STEPMOTHER

"THOMAS," said Abe's stepmother, "Abe must go to school."

"But he knows his letters, Sarah, and he can read and spell a little."

"Very little," said Mrs. Lincoln. "He hasn't been to school since you moved to Indiana, and that was three years ago."

"There wasn't any school near enough."

"There is now, right here on Pigeon Creek. And Abe ought to go. He is eleven years old."

"Oh, Abe is getting along all right. He can work as well as a man," said Thomas Lincoln.

"Work isn't everything, Thomas."

"It's enough for Abe. He'll always be a farm hand; he can't be anything else."

"You can't tell me that, Thomas Lincoln! Abe is smart. He loves books and he remembers everything. He can tell every story he ever heard."

"I know he can do that," said Thomas. "He can even tell what the preacher said at meeting." And then Thomas laughed and laughed.

"What are you laughing at?" asked Sarah.

"Why," said Thomas, "yesterday that boy got up on a stump in the corn-field and preached."

"Preached? You don't mean to say Abe preached?"

"I do," said Thomas. "He thought he was alone, but I was in the woods so I just hid behind a tree and listened." Then Mr. Lincoln laughed again.

"Go on! Go on!" said Sarah.

"Well," said Thomas, "Abe acted exactly like the preacher. He made motions like the preacher. He coughed like the preacher. And he actually preached like him, too."

"How could he preach?" asked Mrs. Lincoln.

"He didn't have any one to preach to."

"He didn't have any one to preach to," she added.

"He preached to the corn-stalks, Sarah. And he preached last Sunday's sermon!"

"Did he remember it?"

"He remembered it better than I did."

"Abe is the smartest boy I know," said Sarah.

"He's too smart," said Thomas. "He must stop this preaching. It takes him from his work."

"Thomas, let Abe go to school this winter. He wants to learn. He'll study hard."

"I can't spare him this winter, Sarah. Some land must be cleared for a new field. We need more bread for such a large family."

"I know we do, Thomas, but the land can be cleared in the spring. Abe can stop school when you are ready for him. And you can't work through the heavy snows anyway."

"That's true," said Mr. Lincoln. "But I haven't any money, Sarah. I can't pay a school-master."

"I'll pay for it myself," said Mrs. Lincoln, "with my chicken money."

"You seem determined, Sarah."

"I am determined, Thomas. Abe must go to school."

And to school Abe went!

XVIII

THE SCHOOL ON PIGEON CREEK

THERE were now several families in the Pigeon Creek neighborhood; enough to pay a schoolmaster.

So these settlers had built a school. It was a log house with one room.

At one end of this room there was a large fireplace which was filled with blazing logs in the winter. This made that end of the room too warm and left the other end too cold.

But Abe didn't mind that. He was used to a cold back at home, and so were the other pupils.

The schoolroom wasn't very light, either. It had only two small windows, and they were made of greased paper.

But Abe didn't mind that, and neither did the others, for that's what they had at home.

The pupils sat on benches without backs.
How would you like to sit that way for hours
and hours in your schoolroom?

Well, Abe didn't mind it. None of them did.
They all sat on stools and benches at home. Of
course the Lincoln family had chairs now, but
not enough to go around. So Abe always used
a stool.

At first Abe was in the class with younger
pupils, some only six years old. And Abe was
eleven!

But he didn't care—he was determined to
learn. He studied so hard and learned so fast he
was soon in the older class.

Every night he studied his lessons while his
brother and sisters and cousin were playing.

Mr. Lincoln didn't like to see Abe study
at home, but he couldn't say much because
Mrs. Lincoln wouldn't allow it. She wouldn't
allow the other children to bother Abe, either.

"Abe is studying," she would say, and that settled it.

The Lincolns couldn't afford to burn candles every night, so Abe studied by firelight. He didn't have a pencil so he used burned wood. He didn't have paper so he used a wooden shovel.

You see, he was *determined* to learn.

Mrs. Lincoln was proud of Abe. She told the neighbors how hard he studied and they told their neighbors.

Before long every one in the Pigeon Creek Settlement knew about it, and they all tried to help the boy.

They couldn't do much because they were all poor, and few of them could read or write. But if they had a book they loaned it to Abe.

Was he glad to have these books? Why, that boy would walk miles and miles to borrow a book and miles and miles to return it.

He read every book again and again, until he knew it almost by heart. Then he would tell the stories to his good stepmother who listened eagerly to every word.

So Abe went on studying, reading, learning. And always back of him stood that splendid stepmother, Sarah Johnston Lincoln.

"Abe is studying," she would say. And that settled it.

XIX

AT THE END OF EACH ROW

WHEN spring came Abe had to stop school. His father needed him. A new field had to be made for wheat.

It was just like the house that Jack built. Such a large family meant more bread; more bread meant more wheat; more wheat meant a new field.

A new field meant the cutting down of many giant forest trees. And every tree that fell meant a great heavy log to cut, and a great heavy stump to dig up and burn.

Such hard work kept them all busy, Mr. Lincoln, John, Dennis and Abe. By daylight they were up; by sundown they went home. Then they ate supper and went to bed—all except Abe.

Tired as he must have been he studied every

night, sometimes till midnight and past midnight.

He even took books to the field and read while he was plowing.

"Why, he couldn't do that!" you boys are saying.

But you forget that rough ground and how hard it was on the horses. They had to rest at the end of each row. So that was when Abe read. Not one minute was wasted.

They had to rest at the end of each row

Sometimes he worked arithmetic problems. He always carried a piece of burned wood in his pocket and he wrote on fence rails and ends of logs.

Mr. Lincoln didn't like this, but what could he say? The horses had to rest, didn't they?

Sometimes Abe would make a speech which always delighted John and Dennis. It delighted others, too. Farm-boys in near-by fields would leave their plows and come running to hear Abe speak. He always told funny stories, and the boys would laugh and laugh.

Mr. Lincoln didn't like this, either. "It won't do," he said. "You are taking the boys away from their work."

"They work all the harder afterward," said Abe. "They laugh and forget they are tired."

"But I don't want you making speeches," said Mr. Lincoln. "It's time wasted. You can't be a lawyer."

"Maybe I can some day," said Abe. "I'd like to."

"That's nonsense, Abe. You'll never have a chance to study law."

"I'll make the chance," said Abe.

"You can't do it," said Mr. Lincoln. "I can't help you; I'm too poor. All you can ever do is farm work."

"But I want to work with books," said Abe.

"Books!" said his father. "Always books! What is all this studying going to do for you? What do you think you are going to be, anyway?"

"Why," said Abe, "I'm going to be president."

Then Abe laughed, and John laughed, and Dennis laughed, and Mr. Lincoln laughed. It was a good joke. Abe Lincoln, president! Ha, ha, ha, ha!

XX

BORROWED BOOKS

NEW settlers moved to the Pigeon Creek Settlement. They came in big wagons and built log cabins in the woods. They made fields for corn and wheat. They made gardens close to their cabins.

The old settlers went to see them and told them about the church and the school. Then, nine times out of ten, they told them about Abe Lincoln.

"He reads books," they said. "He reads by the light of fire, and he reads till midnight and past midnight."

"Till midnight!" said the new settlers. "Till past midnight! Why, we never heard anything like it."

"We lend him our books," the old settlers said. "He will walk miles to borrow them."

"Will he return them?" the new settlers asked.

"Yes," said the old settlers, "he always returns them. And he brings them back as good as they were when he borrowed them."

Then the new settlers looked through their things. If they found a book they lent it to Abe who always returned it. And the book was always as good as it was when he borrowed it.

Once Abe borrowed *The Life of George Washington*. He was delighted with this book, and he made up his mind then and there that he would try to be like Washington; always honest and always loyal to his country.

He read on and on, till midnight and past midnight. Then he had to go to bed, but he took the book to the loft with him.

"I'll read it in the morning," he said to himself, "before the others are up."

He put the book in a crack between two logs.
Then he went to sleep.

That night there was a snow-storm, and the
snow blew into the loft through the wide cracks.

Abe woke up early. What was this? Snow
on his bed! Snow on the floor! And, dear me!
snow on *The Life of George Washington!*

Abe felt very bad. The pages were not wet,
but the book cover was ruined. He knew he
ought to pay for the book. But poor Abe had
no money.

So what did Abe do? Did he pretend he had
lost the book? Did he pretend some one had
taken it?

No indeed! Abe took that book straight to
the owner and explained the ruined cover. Then
he offered to work for the man until the book was
paid for.

"Very well," said the man. "You may work
three days in my corn-field."

Abe worked the three days from sunrise til
sunset. And then he had a big surprise. Th
man gave him the book!

Abe was delighted. He took the book hom
and read it again and again. And every tim
he read it he became more and more determine
to be like General George Washington, twic
President of the United States.

XXI

GAMES ON PIGEON CREEK

PERHAPS you are thinking that Abe studied all the time that he wasn't working. But he didn't! No indeed!

He was just like the other boys on Pigeon Creek when it came to having fun. He played games with them, he ran races, he jumped, he lifted, he wrestled.

These boys were all farm-boys. They worked in the fields and woods, and they were very strong. But Abe Lincoln was the strongest of them all.

He could run faster than any of them. "That is because my legs are so long," he said.

He could jump higher than any of them. "That is because my neck is so long," he said.

He could move heavier logs than any of them.

"That is because my arms are so long," he said.

He could throw any of them when they wrestled. "That is because my hands are so big," he said.

You can see from this that Abe never bragged about himself. And you know that the boys liked him for that. They liked him, too, because he never cheated, and because he was fair to each side.

They saw that they could always trust Abe, so they made him their leader.

Now, these boys didn't study very hard when they were in school, and they didn't read books between times or at any time.

"What good will books do us?" they said. "We'll have to work in the fields all of our lives."

They couldn't understand that farm work wouldn't seem half as hard if they would only read between times. So of course they couldn't understand why Abe studied so hard and why he liked to read books.

But they could understand his strength in games and they talked about it a great deal.

Then their fathers wanted Abe to work for them. And Abe did work for them, and they paid him.

Abe was glad then that he was so strong and that his father had taught him to work when he was a little boy.

He took his money home, and gave it to his father. He was glad he could help his folks.

XXII

THE PREACHER COMES

IT WAS late in the afternoon, but Abe was still working in the forest. He was cutting down trees and he had been working all day.

He was tired and he wanted to stop. He looked at the sun. No, he couldn't stop now. The sun was still above the tree-tops. Abe could tell the time by the sun as well as you can by your clock.

Now Abe was alone in the woods. He might have stopped work. There was no one to see and no one to tell. But Abe was honest. He kept right on chopping.

"Abe! Abe!" some one called.

"Here I am!" called Abe.

A minute later his sister Sarah came down the path.

"Abe," she said, "guess who has come!"

"I can't guess," said Abe. "Who is it?"

"It's the preacher!" Sarah said. "He's going to stay for supper and all night."

"I'm glad," said Abe. "I like to hear him talk. But I can't stop work for an hour or so."

"Father said for you to stop now," said Sarah.

"Stop now!" said Abe, "I can't understand that."

"I can't either," said Sarah, "but that's what he said. He wants you to come right away. And mother said to wash before you come in the cabin."

"I always do, don't I?"

"Sometimes you forget, Abe."

"Maybe I do sometimes."

Then Abe swung his ax over his shoulder and went home with Sarah.

He washed extra good. He combed his hair extra good. Then he went into the cabin.

"Here is Abe," said Mrs. Lincoln, but she didn't smile.

"The preacher has something to say to you, Abe," said Mr. Lincoln, and he didn't smile.

"Good evening, Abe," said the preacher, and he didn't smile either.

Abe couldn't understand. The preacher had always joked and laughed with him—every time he came.

"Pastor," said Mr. Lincoln, "tell Abe just what you came for."

The preacher looked at Abe. "Abe," he said, "I heard that you had been making fun of me. You preached and you made the boys laugh."

"Oh—oh, yes," said poor Abe.

"You coughed just as I do," said the preacher, "and the boys laughed at that."

"Oh—oh, yes," said poor Abe again.

"And you stood as I do, one leg out, the other leg in. Didn't you?"

"Yes, sir," said Abe.

"And worst of all, you blew your nose as I do. Didn't you?"

"Yes, sir," said Abe. "But really I wasn't making fun of you, sir. I was just trying to preach."

"That was it," said Mrs. Lincoln. "Abe wanted to preach, and so, of course, he tried to copy you. He didn't know any other way."

"Sarah, you are always making excuses for Abe," said Mr. Lincoln.

"You laughed at Abe's preaching yourself, Thomas," said Mrs. Lincoln.

Thomas didn't know what to say to this. So he said, "Never mind, we won't talk about that." Then he turned to the preacher and said, "Pastor, I'm going to whip Abe for making fun of you."

"Thomas!" said Mrs. Lincoln, "don't whip Abe! He didn't know he was doing wrong."

Mr. Lincoln didn't answer her. He took a leather strap from a peg.

"Abe," he said, "go out in the yard."

Abe crossed to the door. Mr. Lincoln followed him.

Suddenly a strong hand seized Mr. Lincoln's arm and took the leather strap.

"Don't touch the boy!" said the preacher. "I was only joking. I thought you knew that. Abe was really helping me when he tried to preach."

"Helping you!" said Mr. Lincoln. "I don't understand."

"Why," said the preacher, "every one of those boys came to meeting last Sunday."

"They just went to make fun of you," said Mr. Lincoln.

"Of course," said the preacher. "But they stayed, and some of them joined the church. I never held such a meeting. It was splendid."

"Well, well!" said Mr. Lincoln, "I'm surprised."

"I'm not surprised," said Mrs. Lincoln.

Abe didn't say anything. He didn't know what to say.

The preacher put his arm around Abe. "My boy," he said, "just go on preaching. Your jokes will do a lot of good in the world."

XXIII

THE MUD TURTLE

ONE day Abe went to the creek to fish. He didn't fish with his hands now. He had a pole, and line, and hook.

On the bank stood four boys. They were looking at something on the ground, and they were laughing and shouting.

"I wonder what they are looking at," Abe said to himself.

He went up to them and looked over their heads.

There, on the ground, was a large mud turtle. Its shell had been broken. It was trying to crawl, but it couldn't. It could only jerk and quiver.

Abe saw that it was suffering, and he was very angry. He knew one of the boys had hurt it.

He pushed the boys back. "Stand back!" he said. "Let me have that turtle!"

"You can't have it!" said the largest boy. "It's my turtle. I found it."

"You broke its back, didn't you?" said Abe.

"Yes, I did," said the boy. "I wanted to see how it would crawl. I knew it would look funny."

"I wonder how you would crawl if I broke your back," said Abe. "I wonder if you would look funny."

The boy saw that Abe was very angry, and he was afraid of him. He knew how strong Abe was, because he had seen him wrestle. So he didn't say another word. And he didn't laugh again, either.

The other boys stopped laughing, too. They were all afraid of Abe.

Abe picked up the turtle gently and put it into the creek.

Then Abe said, "Boys, God made that mud turtle. Do you think he wanted you to hurt it?"

The boys hung their heads.

"Do you think God would laugh at its poor broken back?"

The boys still looked at the ground. They were ashamed to look at Abe.

Abe went on: "Do you think God laughed when it quivered and jerked?"

There was silence for a moment, then a boy said, "I am sorry I laughed, Abe."

"I am sorry I laughed," said another boy.

"I am sorry, too," said another.

"I didn't know a turtle suffered," said the largest boy. "It's nothing but an animal."

"Animals suffer just as much as we do," said Abe. "I found a dog once, with a broken leg. It was crying just like a child. No child could have suffered more."

"I'll never hurt an animal again," said the

largest boy. "If I do you may lick me, Abe."

"That is just what I will do," said Abe.

And he meant it. And the boys knew that he meant it.

XXIV

A SPELLING MATCH

"ARE you going to the spelling match to-night, Abe?"

"Of course I'm going, Dennis. I'll be ready in two minutes."

"Oh, yes," said Dennis, but his voice sounded queer. Abe thought Dennis looked queer, too.

"Why did you ask me that, Dennis? You know I always go to spelling matches."

"There's no use for you to go to-night, Abe. They won't let you spell."

"Won't let me spell! Who won't let me spell?"

"The schoolmaster. I met him in the woods this morning. He told me to tell you not to come."

"I haven't missed a word all winter," said Abe. "The side I'm on always wins."

"That is just what he said, Abe. He said it wasn't a match when you came—the other side didn't need to try."

That pleased Abe. "I know the spelling-book forward and backward," he said.

"You're the best speller on Pigeon Creek," said Dennis. "Every one knows that."

That pleased Abe, too. "Well," he said, "I'll go, but I'll just sit and listen."

"I guess that will be all right," said Dennis. The two boys went through the woods to the schoolhouse. They found it full of people— mothers, fathers, uncles, aunts, girls and boys. Every one was talking and laughing. They loved these spelling matches, and they would come from miles around. They would come through dark forests. They would cross dark creeks. Neither rain nor snow could keep them at home. They came early, too, so they could visit with one another.

"There isn't any such wor

in my speller," said Dennis.

Abe and Dennis were late. They were hanging up their hats when the schoolmaster rang a bell. At once there was silence.

The schoolmaster stood on the platform. "Jenny Springer!" he called.

Jenny stood up.

"Jenny," he said, "you have the first choice to-night. Begin."

"Abe Lincoln!" called out Jenny.

"No," said the schoolmaster. "Abe can't spell to-night. It isn't a match when he spells. His side is sure to win. Please choose some one else, Jenny."

Now Jenny was a good girl, but she couldn't understand many things. She didn't know whether the world was round or flat. She thought there was a man in the moon. She thought a pound of sugar weighed more than a pound of feathers. So of course Jenny couldn't understand why Abe shouldn't spell.

"I want Abe!" she cried. "I won't choose any one else!"

"No! No!" cried some voices.

"Abe! Abe!" cried other voices.

The schoolmaster rang his bell. Again there was silence. Abe stood up.

"Jenny," he said, "you must choose some one else. I shall obey the master."

Jenny knew that Abe always obeyed the schoolmaster, so she chose some one else at once.

"Thank you, Abe," whispered the master. "Now sit down and enjoy yourself."

And Abe did enjoy himself. He knew how to spell every word that was missed. When Dennis tried to spell *afraid,* he just had to laugh.

"Afeared," said Dennis.

"No," said the master, "the word is afraid."

"There isn't any such word in my speller," said Dennis. "It's afeared."

"Ha, ha, ha!" laughed Abe.

* * * * * * *

After the match was over the two boys started home. There was no moon and it was very dark in the woods.

"Dennis," said Abe, "are you *afeared?*"

"No," said Dennis, "I'm not even *afraid.*"

They both laughed and went through the dark woods whistling.

XXV

JOHNNY APPLESEED

IT WAS late in the afternoon when Matilda Johnston came out of the Lincoln cabin and started toward the corn-field. Just then Abe and John Johnston came out of the woods and Matilda ran to meet them.

"I came after you," she said. "I thought you were here. I knew you'd like to know."

"Know what?" asked John and Abe.

"Somebody's come," said Matilda, "and he's going to stay for supper. Guess who?"

"The preacher," said Abe.

"No," said Matilda.

"The schoolmaster," said John.

"No," said Matilda.

"I can't guess," said John.

"Neither can I," said Abe.

"It's Johnny Appleseed!" said Matilda.

"Johnny Appleseed!" said Abe. "I've always wanted to see him."

"So have I," said John. "I've heard he's queer."

"He looks mighty strange to me," said Matilda. "He's got his appleseeds."

They went into the cabin and there sat the queerest man they had ever seen in all their lives.

He wore a coffee sack with holes cut in it for his arms. He was barefooted. His hair was long—to his shoulders. At his feet were two large bags filled with appleseeds.

He smiled at the boys and asked them if they could lift his bags. John tried, but he couldn't lift either one. Then Abe tried and lifted both.

The stranger was surprised. "Well! Well!" he said. "I didn't think any boy could lift my bags."

"They are heavy," said Abe. "Have you carried them far?"

"Five hundred miles," said Johnny.

"Just think of that!" said Mrs. Lincoln. "Five hundred miles through the forest with two heavy bags on your back."

"And then you give your seeds away," said Mr. Lincoln.

"Yes, I give them away," said Johnny. "I want to help people, and this is my way of doing it. There are only a few apple trees in this part of the country."

"And they grew from the seeds you brought here," said Mrs. Lincoln.

"I'd like to see an apple orchard near every cabin," Johnny answered. "It would make the settlers love their homes better. Besides, apple trees will bring more settlers here."

"That's true as the Gospels," said Mr. Lincoln.

"What do you do when you are out of seeds?" asked Abe.

"I go back for more," said Johnny, "to the cider mills across the mountain."

"To Pennsylvania?" asked John.

"Yes," said Johnny.

"That's another five hundred miles," said Abe.

"It doesn't matter," said the strange man. "I'm always coming and going."

"Aren't you afraid of Indians?" asked Matilda.

"They have never harmed me."

"But there are snakes in the forest," said Matilda. "Aren't you afraid of them?"

The man looked at his bare feet. "They are tough as leather," he said. "I could stick pins in them and never feel it. I could step on thorns and never know it."

"But there's the cold and the heat and the storms," said Mr. Lincoln.

"I fear nothing," said Johnny, "nothing in the

world. I trust in the Lord to protect me."

Supper was now ready, and they all sat down at the long table. The visitor thanked the Lord for the food they were about to eat.

The meat was passed to him first, but he refused it. "The children must be helped first," he said.

"There is plenty for them," said Mrs. Lincoln.

"I must see it on their plates," said Johnny. "I never eat until I know what the children have."

Mr. Lincoln helped the children. Then the visitor took the meat and ate.

After supper Mr. Lincoln said he wanted to buy some appleseeds.

"You may have all the seeds you want but not one cent will you pay," said Johnny.

"I would rather pay," said Mr. Lincoln.

"You have already paid me," said Johnny.

"You have given me a good supper." Then he arose to go.

"But you must stay all night," said Mrs. Lincoln.

"Of course you must stay all night," said Mr. Lincoln.

"No, no!" cried Johnny. "I must be on my way."

"Where will you sleep?" asked Mr. Lincoln.

"On the ground," said the strange man, "and thank the Lord that I can."

He gave Mr. Lincoln some appleseeds. He thanked Mrs. Lincoln for her good supper. He told them all good-by and went out into the dark forest alone and unafraid.

"I wish I could do something for people, too," said Abe.

"Maybe you will some day, Abe," said his mother.

XXVI

HOW NEIGHBORS HELPED

A NEW settler had come to Pigeon Creek with his family; his wife and two young children. They came in a covered wagon and camped out near the Lincolns'.

The stranger began at once to make a clearing. That done he got logs ready for his cabin. But he couldn't lift them and put them in place. No one man could do that.

This stranger had no money to pay helpers. How then could he ever hope to have a cabin?

There was only one way; he hoped the old settlers would help him.

And he did not hope in vain. The word was passed along that the newcomer was ready.

The news went up and down the creek. The miller told his customers. They told their neighbors, and they, in turn, told their neighbors. It wasn't long until every one had heard the news.

It was good news, too. It gave the settlers a chance to visit with one another all day, for they always took their dinners.

At last the day came. Large baskets were packed with food. Every one put on clean clothing. The men and boys wore their best coonskin caps and moccasins. The women and girls wore their best linsey-woolsey dresses and sunbonnets.

From far and near they came. Some riding horseback, some in big wagons, some, like the Lincolns, walking.

Then the cabin was begun. The men worked hard and the boys helped when they could. They couldn't do much because they couldn't move the logs. Abe was the only boy who could work along with the men.

He helped the preacher with a log. Then he

helped the schoolmaster and the miller. When he saw little Mr. Bigger puffing and panting, he helped him. When he saw big Mr. Little panting and puffing, he helped him. Abe was here, and there, and everywhere.

By noon the cabin was as high as Abe's head. The women had been busy with the dinner. It was spread on long red table-cloths on the ground, and every one sat on the ground to eat.

There were roast venison, turkey and duck. There were pigeon-pie, and stewed pumpkin, and honey. There were wild strawberries and wild grapes. There were apples from the seeds Johnny Appleseed had planted. There were walnuts, hazelnuts and hickory nuts. There was maple sugar in gourds, and there were piles and piles of corn-cakes.

Every one ate and ate, and every one talked and talked.

The preacher told a joke which made every

The women had been busy with the dinner

one laugh. The schoolmaster told a joke, too, and every one laughed again. Mr. Lincoln told an Indian story. Abe told two funny stories which he made up himself.

After dinner the men and boys rested a while. Then the work began again. Log after log was lifted and put in place. Again Abe was here, and there, and everywhere.

Before sunset the cabin was finished. The new settler took his furniture from the big wagon and put it in the new cabin.

He thanked the old settlers again and again. His wife thanked them, and they both thanked the women for the good dinner.

Then every one started home—some horseback, some in big wagons, some walking through the woods.

Dennis Hanks, Sarah and Abe Lincoln, John, Matilda and Sarah Johnston walked with other girls and boys—all talking, laughing, singing.

Mr. and Mrs. Lincoln left them and went ahead.

"I'm proud of the way Abe worked," said Mr. Lincoln. "Every one wanted him to help them."

"Every one likes Abe," said Mrs. Lincoln.

"They like him because he is so strong," said Mr. Lincoln.

"That isn't the only reason, Thomas. They like Abe also because he is smart and good-natured and polite. He will always have friends and good friends, too."

XXVII

MOVING TO ILLINOIS

Mrs. Sarah Lincoln stood alone in the little cabin in the Pigeon Creek Settlement. The room was empty. The bureau, chairs and stools were gone. The dishes, pots and water buckets were gone. The feather-beds, quilts and spinning-wheel were gone. Mr. Lincoln's guns were gone. There wasn't even a coonskin cap hanging on a peg.

Mrs. Lincoln looked about the empty room and began to cry. Just then Thomas came in. "Come, Sarah," he said, "the wagon is loaded and we are ready to start." Then he saw the tears in her eyes. "Why, what is the matter?" he asked.

"I don't want to go," she said. "We've been so happy here. And I love our neighbors; I don't want to leave them."

"But I can't make a living here," said Thomas. "I thought this land was good, but it isn't. I can't raise a good crop of anything."

"I know, but I hate to leave Indiana," said Sarah.

"We'll get rich in Illinois, Sarah. They say everything over there grows twice as fast and twice as large. So we'll have all the money we want, and you shall have a new Sunday dress."

Sarah smiled and dried her eyes. Then she followed Thomas outside. There stood the big wagon drawn by four oxen. It was loaded with furniture, feather-beds, quilts, skins, clothing, tools, shovels, saws, and many other things. There was even a plow.

There was scarcely room for Mrs. Lincoln but she climbed up and sat on the load. Matilda and Sarah Johnston walked by the wagon. They were large and strong and could walk miles and miles without getting tired.

Pretty Sarah Lincoln wasn't with them. She had died two years before.

John Johnston, Dennis Hanks and Abe Lincoln were young men now, but they went with the family and walked with Mr. Lincoln. They kept the oxen in the road with short sticks.

At night they camped in the woods. After supper they all sat around the camp-fire and told stories. Mr. Lincoln told Indian stories. He always knew a new one. Abe told funny stories. He always knew a new one, too.

John, Dennis and Abe took turns watching the fire. This time Abe didn't burn all the wood in one big blaze. He kept a small fire burning, but no green eyes came nearer and nearer.

One day they crossed a small river. It was cold weather and the river was full of floating ice.

When they reached the other side they heard a dog barking. And there across the river—on

the shore they had just left—was their own dog.
They called him, but the dog was afraid to
swim. He was afraid of the floating ice. He
ran up and down the shore barking pitifully.
He was trying to say, "Don't leave me here

The dog was wild with joy

The wagon had gone

alone! There is no one here to take care of me.
I shall starve to death."

"Just listen to him," said Abe. "I can't stand
it. I'm going back for him."

"No, Abe," said his father. "We haven't
time, we must go on."

"I'll catch up with you," said Abe.

Into the icy river he plunged and swam to the
other shore. The dog was wild with joy. He
licked Abe's hands, he jumped, he pranced, he
barked joyfully.

Then into the icy river Abe plunged again. He
held the dog up out of the water and swam with

one arm. It was hard work, but he reached the other shore safely.

The wagon had gone, but Abe overtook it. He put the dog in the wagon and walked on with the men.

"He is tender-hearted," said Mrs. Lincoln. "No one else would have crossed that icy river to get a dog."

"Abe couldn't let the dog starve to death," said Matilda. "The others didn't even think of that."

"That is what makes Abe different," said her mother. "He thinks of everything."

XXVIII

IN THE NEW COUNTRY

THE Lincoln family now lived in a new country, Illinois. Mr. Thomas Lincoln had bought land on the Sangamon River and had built his cabin on the river bank.

Abe had helped him clear land for the cabin and a field. He had helped him build the log cabin and fence in the field.

Then Abe left home. He was now twenty-one years old and he wanted to make a living for himself.

"You have been a great help to me, Abe," said his father. "You have given me every cent you ever earned. I wish I could help you now, but I can't."

"I'm sorry to see you go, Abe," said his step-mother. "You have been so good to me. You have never given me a cross word, and you have

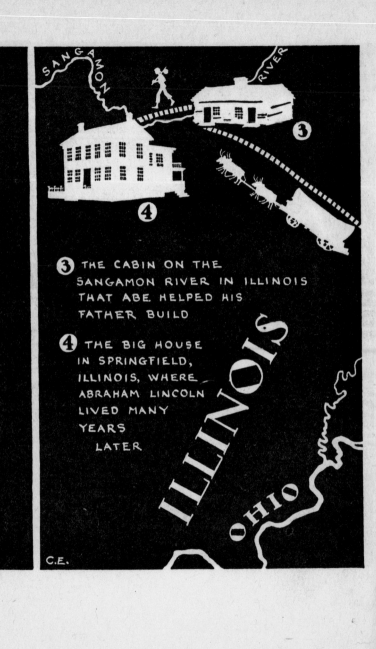

③ THE CABIN ON THE SANGAMON RIVER IN ILLINOIS THAT ABE HELPED HIS FATHER BUILD

④ THE BIG HOUSE IN SPRINGFIELD, ILLINOIS, WHERE ABRAHAM LINCOLN LIVED MANY YEARS LATER

C.E.

1 THE LINCOLNS' CABIN ON KNOB CREEK IN KENTUCKY

2 THEIR CABIN ON LITTLE PIGEON CREEK IN INDIANA

IIIIIIIIIIIIIII SHOWS ABE'S JOURNEYS FROM THE LOG CABIN ON KNOB CREEK, WHERE HE LIVED WHEN HE WAS A LITTLE BOY, TO THE BIG HOUSE IN SPRINGFIELD

INDIANA

RIVER

LITTLE PIGEON CREEK

KENTUCKY

never disobeyed me. I love you as if you were my own son."

"You have been good to me, mother," said Abe. "I will never forget you, and I will help you as long as I live."

Abe carried his clothes in a small bundle. This he tied to a stick which he carried over his shoulder. He may have had a little money, maybe twenty-five cents.

He found plenty of work on farms near by. He plowed, chopped down trees and split rails. He husked corn, took care of horses, cows and pigs. He did every kind of work that was done on a farm.

If there was no farm work to be done, he would then help the farmer's wife. He carried water, dug potatoes, fed the chickens and churned.

He even took care of the children. And he didn't mind rocking the baby to sleep because it gave him a chance to read. He rocked the cradle with his foot, you see.

And so Abe worked and worked. From sunrise to sunset he worked. But he was never too tired to tell funny stories and jokes. And he was never too tired to be kind to every one.

Before long Abe had many new friends. They invited him to Sunday dinner; they told him to stop in when he was passing by. They liked Abe because he wasn't rough and quarrelsome. But most of all they liked him because he was kind.

One cold day Abe saw a man chopping wood. The man was barefooted and his clothing was old and thin. He was shivering with the cold and he looked unable to work at all.

Abe felt very sorry for this poor man.

"How are you this cold day?" he asked.

"I'm just about ill," said the man, "but I have to chop this wood. I need shoes."

"Give me that ax," said Abe, "and go home and sit by the fire."

The man thanked Abe and went home at once.

Then Abe swung the ax. And there were few who could swing an ax as Abe could. He knew just how high to lift it. He knew just how hard to strike.

So it wasn't long until the great pile of wood was chopped. And it wasn't long either until the poor man sold it and bought shoes.

Do you think he loved Abe Lincoln? Indeed he did. He was devoted to Abe as long as he lived.

XXIX

HELPING THE HELPLESS

"MOLLY," said the cooper to his wife, "Abe Lincoln has a new suit of clothes."

"Well! Well!" said Molly. "I'm glad to hear that. If ever any one in this world deserves a new suit it's that young man."

"That's exactly what I think," said the cooper.

"But how did he ever get enough money to buy a suit?" asked Molly.

"He split rails, Molly. Every yard of the goods cost him one week of hard work."

"He must have split hundreds," said Molly.

"He must have," said the cooper. "But it was time he got a good suit. They were making fun of his clothes."

"Who was?" asked Molly sharply. She liked Abe, and she didn't want any one to make fun of him.

"Oh, the folks who don't want Abe to succeed," said the cooper.

"Of course," said Molly. "They are jealous of Abe because he can make better speeches than any of them."

"Indeed he can," said the cooper. "Abe Lincoln is the best speaker in this state. He is going to speak at the Big Meeting next week."

"I hope he will wear his new suit," said Molly.

"He will. That's why he bought it. He told me so himself."

"Well, no one need be ashamed of Abe Lincoln in his old clothes," said Molly.

Mr. Abe Lincoln was on his way to the Big Meeting. He wore his new suit, and he was proud of it. "They can't make fun of me today," he said to himself. "I look as well as any of them now."

He was riding horseback on a muddy road,

and he rode carefully. He didn't want his new clothes splashed with mud.

Just then he heard a pig squeal. He looked around and there in a field, in a great mud-hole was a little pig.

It was struggling to get out of the mud, but it couldn't. It looked straight into Abe's eyes and squealed again.

Abe said, "I am very sorry, little pig, but I can't help you. This is my new suit, and you would ruin it. I hope some one else will get you out."

Then Abe rode on. But he couldn't forget that pitiful squeal. He couldn't forget the fear in the little pig's eyes.

Suddenly he turned his horse and rode back. He pulled the pig out of the mud and put him on dry land.

And that was fine for the pig, wasn't it? But what about Mr. Lincoln's new suit? The suit

he had worked so hard to get. The first good
suit he had ever owned.

Mr. Lincoln arrived at the Big Meeting with
mud-spattered clothes. He was late. The people had been waiting for him a long time. They
were shouting for him now. "Abe! Abe!" they
shouted. "Speech! Speech!"

Mr. Lincoln brushed his clothes, but the mud
stains showed plainly.

He couldn't keep the people waiting any
longer so he went on the platform and began his
speech.

In two minutes every one forgot the muddy
clothes. Mr. Abe Lincoln was speaking
Nothing else mattered.

XXX

THE LITTLE TRUNK

SEVERAL years passed. Mr. Abe Lincoln still
lived in Illinois, but he didn't live in a cabin
in the woods. He lived in a two-story house in
a big town, Springfield.

No longer did Abe plow, chop down trees
and split rails. He was now a lawyer. Do you
hear that? *He was a lawyer.* He had an office
in that big town, and every one respected him
and called him *Mr. Lincoln.* And they didn't
dare to call him anything else.

That is what study and good books did for
Abe.

He still worked hard but it was the kind of
work he loved. He worked with books and he
was helping people.

He would ride horseback many miles to get
some one out of trouble. He would ride on

muddy roads, through rain, sleet and snow.

He still studied at night and sometimes till midnight and past midnight. The more he learned, the more he wanted to learn. He never thought he knew enough.

But he never forgot to tell funny stories and jokes, and he never forgot to be kind. He would go out of his way and neglect his own business to help others.

"Mr. Lincoln helped me once," said an old lady to three little girls.

"Mr. Lincoln! The great Mr. Lincoln?" asked Helen.

"Yes, my dear," said the old lady. "The great Mr. Lincoln. It was when I was a little girl. I lived in the same town, Springfield, and he often passed my home."

"Did he speak to you?" asked Elsie.

"Always, Elsie. He never forgot to look for

me. Mr. Lincoln loved children." Grandma
smiled as she remembered.

"But how did he help you?" asked Helen
again.

"I'll tell you the whole story, girls. I was
going to visit my grandmother in another city.
I had to go on the train and I had to go alone.
My father and mother were too busy to go with
me.

"But they helped me get ready. Mother made
some pretty dresses for me. Father bought a
little trunk."

"A trunk!" said the three girls all together.

"Yes, indeed," said the old lady, "and it wasn't
a toy trunk, either. It was large enough to hold
six dresses, two pairs of shoes, my Sunday hat,
a sunbonnet, and many other things."

"Did you have a Sunday dress?" asked
Mary.

"Yes, my dear, I did. It was pink and I had

pink slippers and pink stockings. My Sunday hat was pink, too."

"I know you looked beautiful, grandma," said Mary.

Grandma smiled again as she remembered something else. "I had a pink parasol, too," she said.

"Did you put it in your trunk?" asked Elsie.

Grandmother nodded. "It was the last thing mother put in," she said. "Then she locked the trunk and father carried it down-stairs. He left it on the porch and went for the expressman.

"I was all ready, so I just sat down and waited. I waited and waited. I talked with mother. Then I waited again, but the expressman didn't come.

"It was almost time for the train, so I went out to the gate to look for him. I looked up the street. I looked down the street. Then I looked up and down and down and up. There wasn't a sign of him!"

"Oh! Oh!" said the girls.

"Then," said grandmother, "I heard the train whistle, and I knew it would soon be at the station."

"Oh! Oh!" said the girls again.

"What did you do, grandma?" asked Elsie.

"I cried, Elsie. I cried out loud, too. I knew I couldn't get the train now.

"Suddenly a tall man crossed the street. He had black hair, gray eyes, and such a kind face."

"Mr. Lincoln!" cried the girls.

"Yes, girls, it was Mr. Lincoln. He said he heard me crying across the street and he wanted to know what was the matter.

"I told him about my trunk and the express-man.

" 'Is it a large trunk?' he asked.

" 'No, it's a small trunk,' I said. 'It's there, on the porch.'

CLOTILDE EMBREE

"Away he hurried

to the station."

" 'I'll take it to the station,' he said. Then he ran to the porch; lifted the trunk to his shoulder, and away he hurried to the station.

"I had to run to keep up with him, but I did keep up, and we reached the station just in time.

"The train was ready to go. The conductor was calling, 'All aboard!'

" 'Wait for this young lady!' called Mr. Lincoln.

"The conductor helped me up the steps. Mr. Lincoln put my trunk in the baggage car. Then the train began to move.

"Mr. Lincoln waved his hat to me and I waved my hand to him. 'He's the kindest man in the world,' I said to myself. And I have said it ever since, girls. He was always the kindest man in the world."

XXXI

ABE LINCOLN: PRESIDENT OF THE UNITED STATES

BELLS rang! Whistles blew! People shouted! Men hugged each other and threw their hats into the air.

"Abe Lincoln is elected!" they cried. "Abe Lincoln is elected President!"

Thousands traveled miles to see him. Thousands waited hours to hear him speak.

Abe Lincoln, once a boy of the backwoods, was now the most honored man of the nation.

Abe Lincoln, once plowing, chopping, splitting rails.

Abe Lincoln, once studying by firelight, poor, shabbily dressed.

But

Abe Lincoln, always studying, thinking, learning.

Abe Lincoln, always honest, fair in games and work.

Abe Lincoln, always kind to man and beast.

That little boy who lived in a little log cabin on a little farm in a little clearing on a little creek, was now out of the forest and into the world of cities and men.

He had become one of the greatest men this world had ever known. A great nation loved him. The whole world had heard of him and admired him.

"Only of such a boy were made
The loving man he was."

THE END

Date Due

MAY 1 4 '54			
OCT 1 2 '56			
FEB 21 '6			
NOV 8 '65			
NOV 20 '65			
DEC 14 '65			
MAR 2 2 '66			
APR 29 '66			